THE MOST PATIENT MAN

Quran Stories for Little Hearts

by

S Khan

Goodword**kidz**

Helping you build a family of faith

ARABIA

ARABIAN GULF

3

The Prophet Ayyub ﷺ, a great prophet who lived in the ninth century B.C. in Haran near Damascus in Syria, set great examples for mankind.

Besides having great wisdom and compassion,
Ayyub  was also a very rich man.

8

He had huge herds of cattle, vast fields, a large family and many friends. Yet, he remained an extremely steadfast and sincere servant of Allah, and was forever calling upon others to worship Him.

But Satan made people think that it was only because Ayyub ﷺ was wealthy that he lived a good life, and that if his blessings were taken away, he would no longer be grateful to Allah.

10

12

To put him to the test, Allah struck him with a series of calamities. His cattle and crops were destroyed, his children died and, worst of all, he became very ill, remaining bedridden for many years.

Within a very short period of time, Ayyub عليه السلام became very poor and his friends left him one by one. But Ayyub عليه السلام was not angry. He put his entire trust in Allah, being confident that Allah knew best about everything.

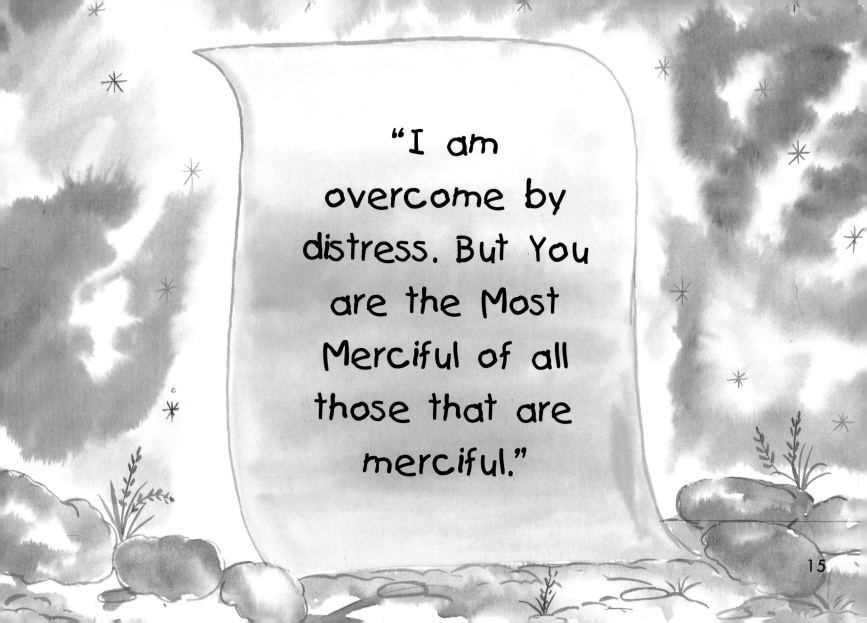

"I am overcome by distress. But You are the Most Merciful of all those that are merciful."

When his suffering and loneliness worsened and his sickness and pain became unbearable, Ayyub عليه السلام turned to Allah in humble prayer, crying: "I am overcome by distress. But You are the Most Merciful of all those that are merciful."

Allah heard his beautiful prayer, and put an end
to his long and terrible hardship. He ordered
Ayyub عليه السلام to strike the ground with his feet.

He did as commanded, and by a miracle, a spring of fresh water gushed forth.

21

No sooner did Ayyub ﷺ take a bath in it, than his illness was cured and he regained his former health and strength.

22

Because Ayyub ﷺ had showed great patience throughout the worst of disasters, Allah not only rewarded him with great bounty in the Hereafter, but redoubled his former prosperity in this world. He had a new family of seven sons and three daughters. He lived to the ripe old age of 93 and saw four generations. He became so rich that it was said that "he was rained upon with locusts of gold."

Find Out More
To know more about the message and meaning of Allah's words, look up the following parts of the Quran which tell the story of the Prophet Ayyub ﷺ (Job).
Surah Sad 38:41-44
Surah al-Anbiya 21:83-84

ﷺ *Alayhis Salam* 'May peace be upon him.' The customary blessing on the prophets.